WONDERFUL
TIME

WONDERFUL TIME

Phyllis McGinley

Illustrated
by John Alcorn

J. B. LIPPINCOTT COMPANY PHILADELPHIA AND NEW YORK

"The Voice of the Clock," "The Face of the Clock," "Clock Manners," "Lengths of Time," "The Missing People," and "A Child's-Eye View of Clocks" were first published in *Vogue Children.*

"Secret Whispered at Bedtime," "Two Queer Timepieces," and "The Answer" were first published in *McCall's.*

Contents

WONDERFUL
TIME

The Question

What is Time?

Is it something to touch like a tree,
A table, a boulder?
Can you see,
From the tail of your eye,
Time strolling by?

Can you *hear* Time
Blowing like wind past your shoulder,
Or smell it like leather
Or taste it, perhaps, on your tongue
Like rolls from a pan?

No, nobody can,
Not the old, not the young.

Yet all of us share
Invisible Time like the air.
It is real as the boulder,
The table, the tree.
It moves and you with it (like me),
Growing up, growing older;
Each of us borne like a boat on
A river of Time which we float on
All our lives long.

And what's most exciting and strange is
That hour by hour it changes
As hour by hour do we.

Although we can't touch it or taste it,
We can save it or use it
Or waste it,
But chiefly we measure it out.

And that is what Clocks are about.

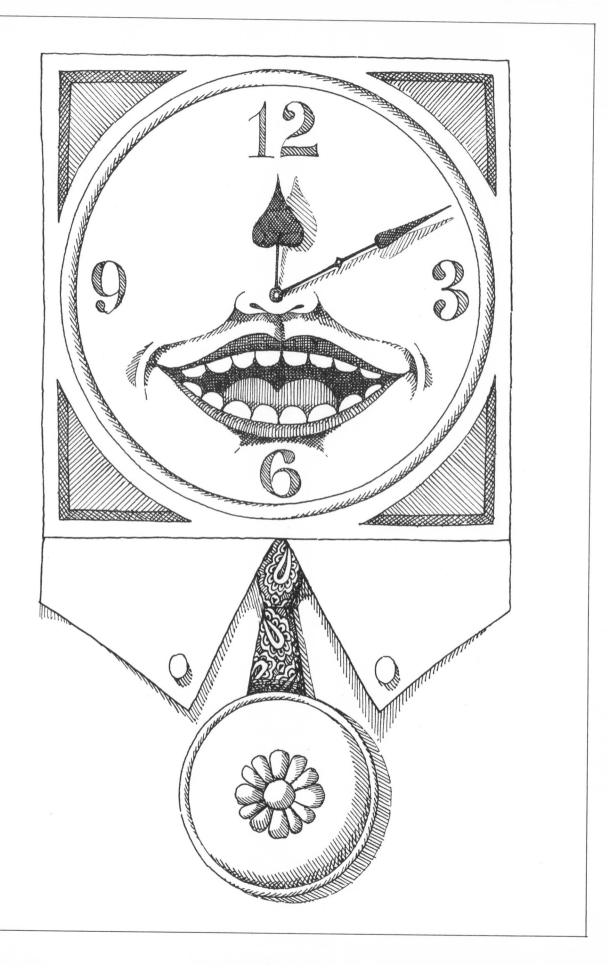

The
Voice
of
the
Clock

"Tick, tock,"
Speaks the Clock
All night
And day.
"Tick, tock,
Dickory-dock."
What does the Clock
Say?

"Tick," it says.
"Chime," it says.
"I
Tell
The time," it says.
"Train Time,
Or plain time
Or time when whistles blow.
Four o'clock
Or nine o'clock
Or time to rise-and-shine o'clock—
I count the minutes
And the hours
As they go.

"Hear the morning's drums again.
This day never comes again.
Wash your face
And brush your teeth
And tie your shiny shoe.
Breakfast's on your plate," it says.
"Don't
Be
Late," it says,
"Else you may be missing
Something wonderful and new.

"Tock," it says.
"Tick," it says.
"Doesn't night come quick?" it says.
"*Did* you have a happy day
And maybe have you grown?
Though you cannot keep a bit
Of time, go off to sleep a bit.
Tomorrow's
Round the corner
With adventures of its own.

"Tick, tock,"
Speaks the Clock,
End–
Less–
Ly.
"I'll mind the hours
If you'll mind me."

The Face of the Clock

1. The Big Hand is busy
   But the Small Hand has power.
   The Large one counts the minutes
   But the Little one names the hour.
   Which only goes to show us all
   That Big's no better off than Small.

2. When both Hands stand at the top together,
   It's sure to be TWELVE O'CLOCK. But whether
   That's twelve at noon or twelve at night
   Depends on if it's dark or light.

3. NINE and THREE
Are easy to see.
The Big Hand's up
As high as can be,
Straight as a soldier,
Guarding a town.

At THREE
The Little Hand's
Halfway down,
Like the soldier's gun
Before he drops it.

But NINE O'CLOCK
Is exactly opp'site.
Perhaps you're at school
Perhaps at play
Or else in bed
At the end of day,
But it's NINE O'CLOCK
Upon the crack
When the Brave Little Hand
Climbs halfway back.

4. When down to the bottom the Little Hand goes,
    Up top the Big Hand's steady,
Come in, spick-spock!
For it's SIX O'CLOCK
    And supper is probably ready.

5. Some folks believe that we should have *more* o'clock,
Since midnight's really TWENTY-FOUR O'CLOCK.
But dials like that? You never see 'em.
There's only TWELVE A.M. or P.M.

Perhaps here's all it may amount to:
TWELVE is the highest Clocks can count to.

Clock
Manners

If children mimicked Clocks,
We'd cry
That they were either rude
Or shy.

A Clock sits stubbornly
In place.
It keeps both Hands
In front of its Face.

Incessantly
Upon the shelf
It chatters, chatters,
To itself

Without a word
For anyone.
It never walks,
Will only run,

And if you ask
The simplest thing,
It points
Instead of answering.

But what makes children
Laughing stocks
Is good behavior
In Clocks.

Shadows

Were there no Clocks at all to tell
Time, you might manage pretty well

By noticing with open eyes
Your shadow change its place and size.

Face east and let the morning find you—
Your shadow stretches tall behind you.

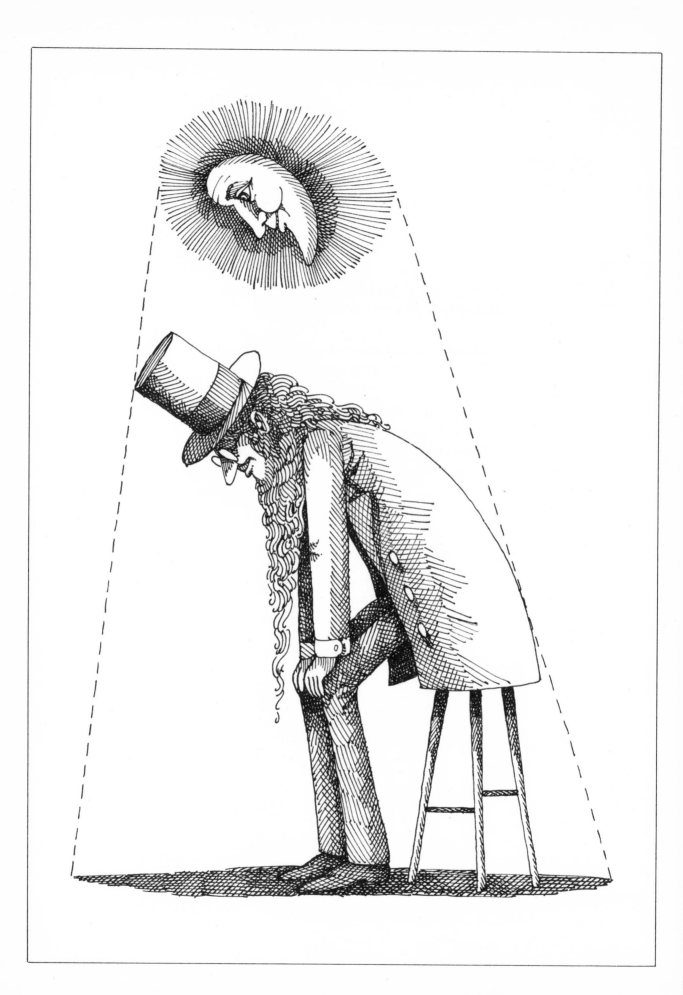

At evening if you look around,
It lies before you on the ground.

At noon it's smaller; it will tend
To walk beside you like a friend.

Though if you lived at the equator,
The difference would be even greater.
There just at noon, you'd stare and stare
But wouldn't find it anywhere.

Lengths of Time

Time is peculiar
And hardly exact.
Though minutes are minutes,
You'll find for a fact
(As the older you get
And the bigger you grow)
That Time can
Hurrylikethis
Or plod,   plod,   slow.

Waiting for your dinner when you're hungry?
Down with the sniffles in your bed?
Notice how an hour crawls along and crawls along
Like a snail with his house upon his head.

But when you are starting
A game in the park,
It's morning,
It's noon,
And it's suddenly dark.
And hours like seconds
Rush blurringly by,
Whoosh!
Like a plane in the sky.

The
Missing
People

People who
Refuse to pay
Attention to
The Time of Day

May be polite
To young or old
And extra bright
And good as gold,

But, no denial,
They appear
A trial
To their near and dear.

And there is eve-
-N worse than this.
You won't be*lieve*
The things they miss.

By dawdling, letting breakfast cool,
They miss the bus that goes to school,

Then late to school they more or less
Miss choosing-up time at recess.

Supper's at six?
They can't be seen.
At treat-or-tricks
On Halloween,

Theirs is the bag'll
Come home light,
So late they straggle
Out that night.

At birthday parties, late by habit,
They miss the magician and his rabbit.

To circuses they come delayed,
So miss the Opening Grand Parade

When elephants march by in bunches.
They miss their snacks, they miss their lunches,

So never get much more than pickin's
Of blueberry pie and roasting chickens.

They miss the dates they make with cronies;
Miss hayrides, sleigh rides, rides on ponies,

Picnics and swims and Sunday drives.
In fact, they're missing half their lives;

For people who
Refuse to pay
Attention to
The Time of Day

May well be nice
To hug or hold,
And maybe twice
As good as gold,

But they miss ships,
Miss shows by dozens,
Miss country trips
To favorite cousins,

Miss games of touch
Or volleyball,
But aren't missed much,
Themselves, at all.

A Child's-Eye View of Clocks

The Grandfather's Clock
Stands stiff and tall
Against the staircase
In the hall.
Every so often
It clears its throat
And gives commands
With a solemn note.
"Come, come, come when I call,"
Booms the Grandfather's Clock in the hall.

The noisy Alarm Clock
Likes to scream
The dreamer out of his
Morning dream.
"Clang," it clatters,
And "Hup, hup, hup!
Today is country day.
Up, get up.
Cling, clang, and off to the farm,"
Shrieks the Clock with the shrilling alarm.

The Clock in the kitchen
Clucks away,
Its round face cheerful
As Saturday.
It beams, "Good morning,"
It ticks, "Have fun."
It knows the minute
A cake is done.
Then, "Come, come, come on and *pitch* in,"
Says the kind Clock in the kitchen.

But the pleasantest timepiece
On the list,
Mother slips quietly
Over her wrist.
It's little and gold
With a tiny tone.
(I wear it, sometimes,
When we're alone.)
"Come, come, come and be kissed,"
Says the little gold Watch on her wrist.

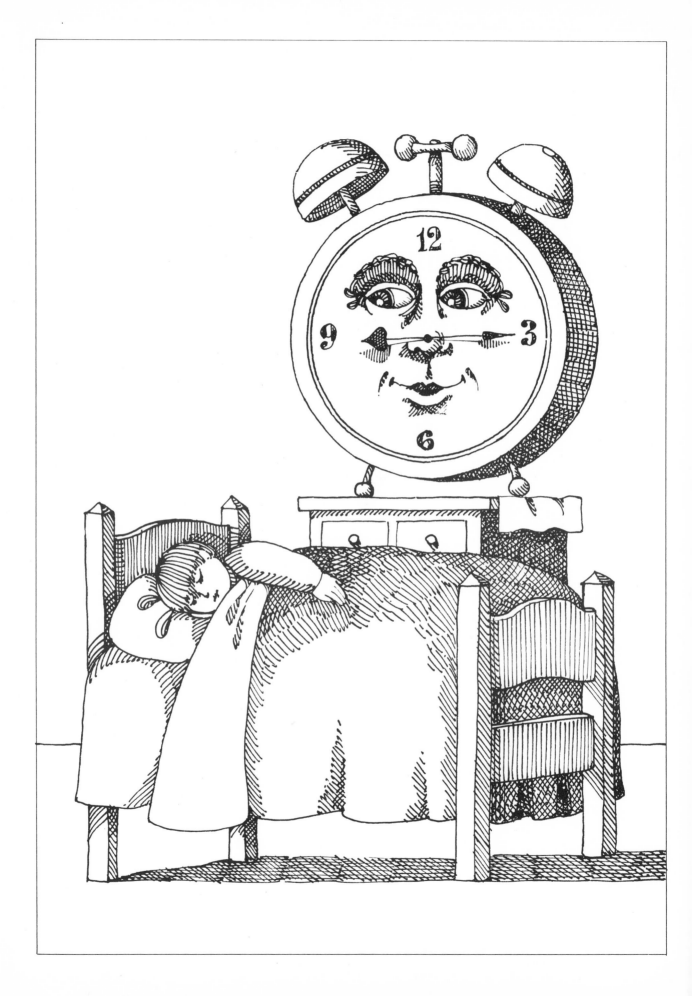

Secret Whispered at Bedtime

Electric Clocks are not
Talkative. They are what
We use, these days, a lot.

They run on current, so
It's seldom that they go
Either too fast or slow.

They hum. They're always right.
Yet humming isn't quite
So cozy in the night

(When dark comes dim and fearful)
As Clocks which tick the ear full
Of sounds serene and cheerful,

Which make the heart rejoice.
I know I'll take by choice
A Clock which has a voice.

Daylight Saving Time

In Spring when maple buds are red,
We turn the Clock an hour ahead;
Which means, each April that arrives,
We lose an hour
Out of our lives.

Who cares? When Autumn birds in flocks
Fly southward, back we turn the Clocks,
And so regain a lovely thing—
That missing hour
We lost last Spring.

Two Queer Timepieces

Before the Clock
Was first invented,
A world of people
Lived contented,
Who measured Time
Or watched it pass
By Sun Dial
Or by Hourglass.

Perhaps you've seen them.
Sun Dials stand
In gardens.
But they have no Hand.
Only a shadow
From the sun
Marks off the hours
As they run.
(At night their trouble
Lies in this:
You cannot tell
What time it is.)

The Hourglass
Is small of waist,
Like a fat lady
Tightly laced.
From head to toe
A sandy shower
Trickles. The journey
Takes an hour.
And when the sand's run out,
Why, then
You turn it over
And start again.

Though useful
In a hundred ways
To people
Of the Olden Days,
The Hourglass,
The Sun Dial, too,
Are things I'm rather
Pleased to do
Without. For Hour-
Glasses sound
Like awkward Watches
To lug around.

You'd have to be stronger
Than Davy Crockett,
To carry a Sun Dial
In your pocket.

Simple Simon's Song

I can see by the Clock
When it's three by the Clock.
I know when it's ten or two.
I can read or spell Time,
But I can't tell Time.
  Neither, my dears, can you.

For all our cleverness,
  All our fuss,
Nobody *tells* Time.
  It tells us!

Why We Have Night and Day and Four Seasons

The world is spinning, spinning,
  While we sleep or play.
First it turns us toward the sun,
  Then the other way.
So half of the time it's nighttime,
  And half of the time it's day.

The world both turns and travels,
  Making a yearly ring
Around the sun and back again,
  Forever on the wing.
So part of the time it's Autumn,
  And part of the time it's Spring.

So certain are the seasons,
  So true are sun and star,
That we can mark them by the Clock
  Or on a Calendar.
Oh, world that spins and journies,
  How wonderful you are.

The Answer

What is Time, then?

It is minutes and seasons and years.
It is giggles and tears,
Enjoyment and things we're afraid of.
It's the stuff we are made of.

Time is Christmas and measles.
It's birthdays, and marking the wall
To show us how tall
We've grown since the birthday before.

It's what we remember and what is arriving or going.
It's a wave which is flowing
Past an invisible shore,
Changing from minute to minute.
It's a sea. And we're all swimming in it,
Borne along, borne along
Toward lands which we wait to explore.

And though we can't touch it
Or hear it
(Or even come near it),
We can save it or use it or measure it.

And if we are wise,
We will treasure it.